788.53 WAR NON-B...

KU-789-138

CONTENTS

In Book 1 you met Franzo Frog and his friends: Denzel Donkey, Ebenezer Elephant, Geraldine Giraffe, Amos Ape, Bertram Bear, Clarissa Cockatoo and Danielle Deer. Their notes which you learned were:

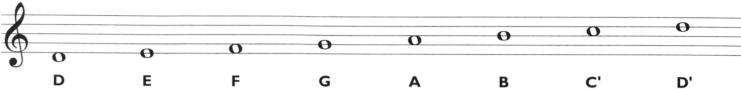

Each one of the friends has a new song in this book.

You will meet two more friends and learn five new notes. You can clap, sing and play all the songs and they all have percussion accompaniments. You might like to make up some percussion accompaniments of your own. The ones in the book are only suggestions to start you off. You could record a tune, then try using different percussion instruments to find which sound best.

The first song, 'Animal alphabet', is to remind you of all the friends and their musical notes. If you have forgotten how to play them, look at the fingering chart at the back of this book on pages 28, 29 and 30.

Try making up some songs about other animals. Give them names, then work out a rhythm and a tune for them: … Herbert Hamster … Henrietta Horse …

Have fun!

Animal alphabet

C is for Cla-ris-sa, Cla-ris-sa Cock-a-too. B is for Ber-tram, Ber-tram Bear.

A is for A-mos, A-mos Ape. G is for Ge-ral-dine, Ge-ral-dine Gi-raffe.

F is for Fran-zo, Fran-zo Frog. E is for Eb-en-e-zer, Eb-en-e-zer El-e-phant.

D is for Den-zel, Den-zel Don-key. High D is for Dan-i-elle, Dan-i-elle Deer.

The last 2 bars of this song are in 2 parts which are played together to make the music sound really good. You can play part ① and a friend can play part ② at the same time. Then change over.

Don't for-get now you've met the a-ni-mal al-pha-bet!

3

||: :|| These are repeat signs. They tell you that you should play the music between these signs twice.

𝅝 ⌣ 𝅗𝅥 This is a tied note sign. It means that you don't play the second note. Instead you play the first note for the total number of beats.

1 2 3 4   1 2

So 𝅝 ⌣ 𝅗𝅥 means you play the first note for 6 beats altogether.

Good friends

We're all good

friends

One, two, three, four, five, six, seven, eight. One, two, three, four,

five, six, seven, eight. We are, we are, we are eight good friends.

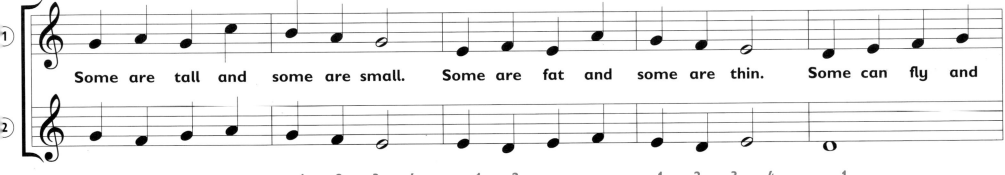

Some are tall and some are small. Some are fat and some are thin. Some can fly and

1 – 2 – 3 – 4 – 1 – 2   1 – 2 – 3 – 4 – 1

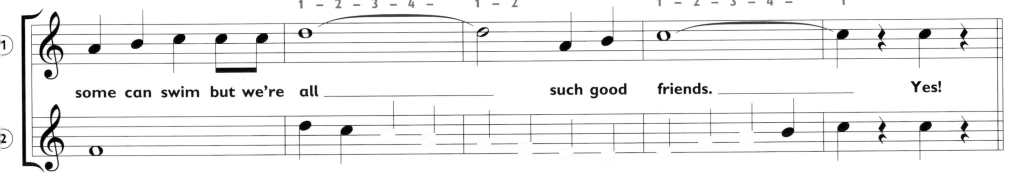

some can swim but we're all _____ such good friends. _____ Yes!

5

Slurs

A slur sign ⌣ joins 2 *different* notes together. This tells you to play the first note and then change the fingering to the second note. You need to do this without tonguing the second note (saying 't') so that both notes are played smoothly in the same breath.

Tied notes

Remember that if both the notes are the *same* and are joined by a ⌣ sign, you don't tongue the second note but hold the first note for the total number of beats.

Breathing sign

√ This sign shows you when to take a breath.

Bertram's beetroot burgers

Ber-tram's Beet-root Bur-gers are the best in town. Made with lots of love-ly on-ions

nice and brown. Take a bite and you will see they're great to eat, e-

-spec-ial-ly when you're real-ly hun-gry, what a treat!

like bur-gers like bur-gers

7

F#

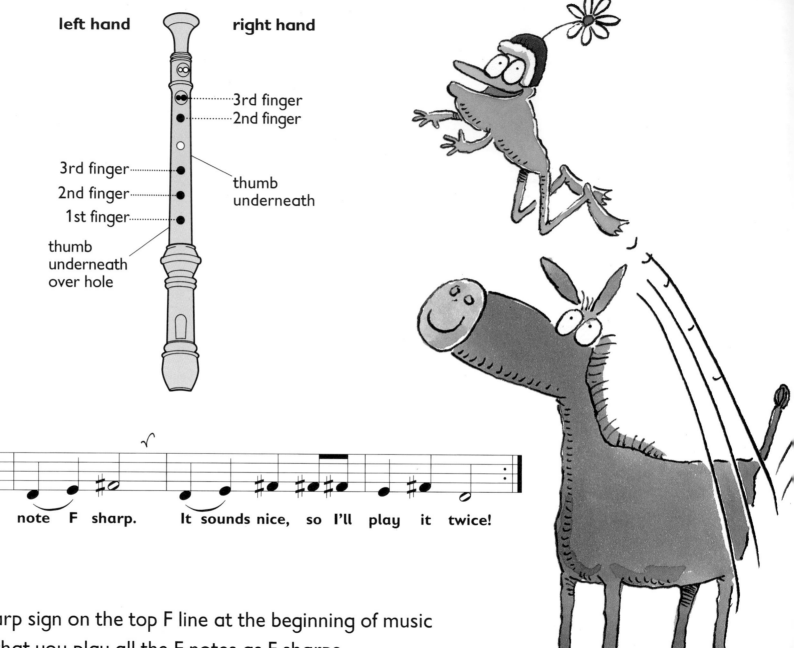

left hand   right hand

3rd finger
2nd finger

3rd finger
2nd finger
1st finger

thumb
underneath

thumb
underneath
over hole

F# (F sharp) is the note
between F and G.
It sounds a bit higher than
F and a bit lower than G.

I can play the note F sharp. It sounds nice, so I'll play it twice!

This sharp sign on the top F line at the beginning of music
means that you play all the F notes as F sharps.

Hello Franzo

Remember to play F♯ in this song.

Fran-zo Frog is al-ways on the go. _____
He is the most live-ly frog I know.

Jump-ing here and jump-ing there, al-ways jump-ing ev-ery-where,

Please stand still, I just want to say hel - lo, _____ hel - lo!

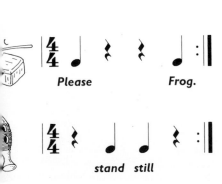

Please Frog.

stand still

A dot under or over a note tells you to stop the sound quickly. This is called staccato.

high E'

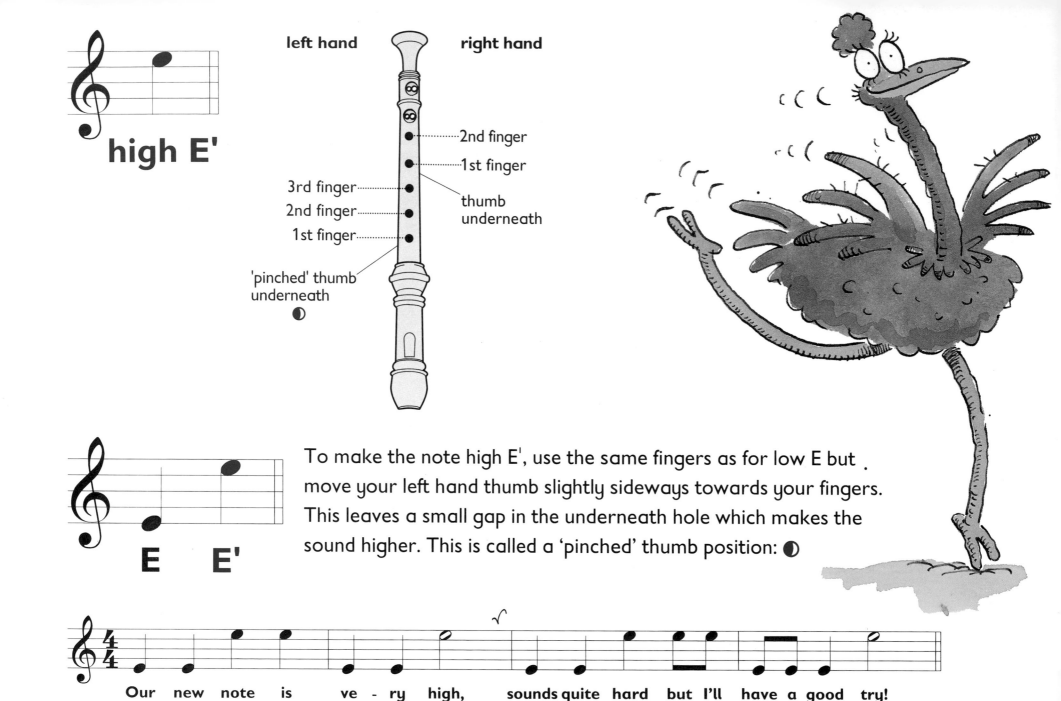

left hand　　**right hand**

- 2nd finger
- 1st finger
- thumb underneath
- 3rd finger
- 2nd finger
- 1st finger
- 'pinched' thumb underneath

E　E'

To make the note high E', use the same fingers as for low E but move your left hand thumb slightly sideways towards your fingers. This leaves a small gap in the underneath hole which makes the sound higher. This is called a 'pinched' thumb position:

Our new note is ve - ry high, sounds quite hard but I'll have a good try!

Emily Emu

Count 6 before you start.

$\frac{6}{8}$ means that there are 6 quavers (half beat notes) in each bar.

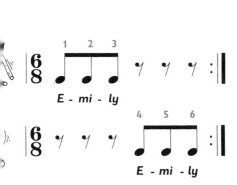

Remember F♯.

'Who are you and what's your name?' 'I'm E - mi - ly E - mu. I

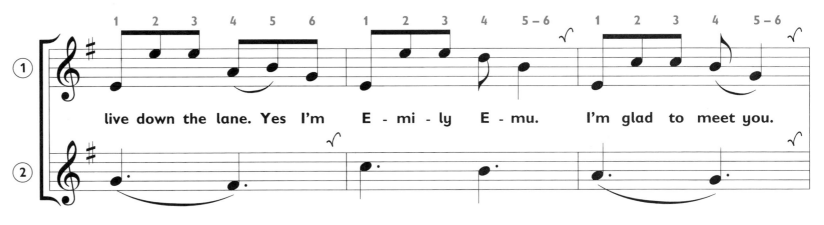

live down the lane. Yes I'm E - mi - ly E - mu. I'm glad to meet you.

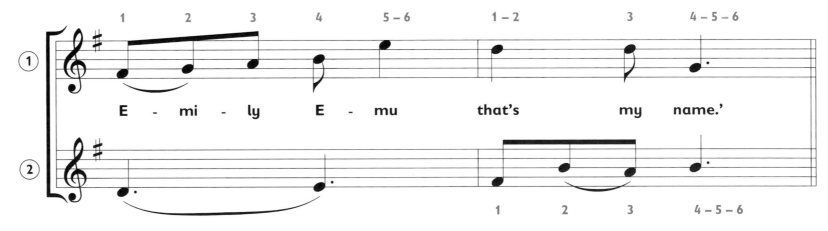

E - mi - ly E - mu that's my name.'

Ebenezer Elephant's aerobics

Come on ev-ery-bo-dy, come on and join the fun. **CLAP** Eb-en-e-zer El-e-phant's aer-

-o-bics have be-gun. **CLAP** 1. Stand up with your legs a-part. One, two, three, four.

Shake your arms and now we'll start. One, two, three, four. Hands on hips lean left and right. One, two, three, four.

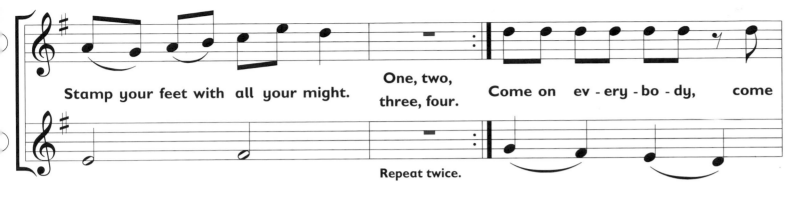

Stamp your feet with all your might. One, two, three, four. Come on ev - ery - bo - dy, come

Repeat twice.

on and join the fun. Eb - en - e - zer El - e - phant's aer - o - bics have be - gun!

CLAP

2. Stretch right down and touch your toes.
Tap your shoulders, then your nose.
Lift your arms and stretch up high.
Point your fingers to the sky.

3. Clap your hands and keep the beat.
Make the music with your feet.
Swing your arms and march along.
Keeping fit and sing my song.

4 beat rest (percussion continues playing).

Eb - en - e - zer, Eb - en - e - zer

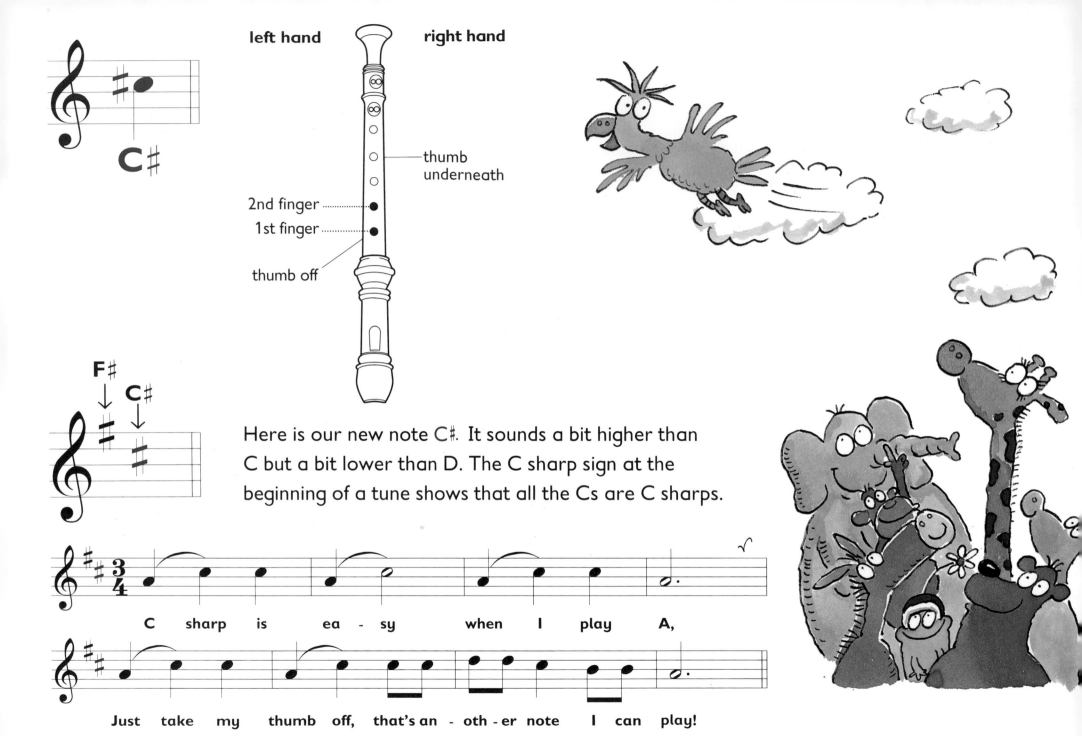

left hand

right hand

C#

thumb underneath

2nd finger

1st finger

thumb off

F# C#

Here is our new note C#. It sounds a bit higher than C but a bit lower than D. The C sharp sign at the beginning of a tune shows that all the Cs are C sharps.

C sharp is ea-sy when I play A,

Just take my thumb off, that's an-oth-er note I can play!

Clarissa's song

Remember to play C♯ and F♯.

* This sign means percussion starts here.

Cock - a - too's song

15

Amos the acrobat

A - mos is an a - cro - bat, he loves to swing thro' the

trees. With squeals of de - light he gives us a fright, we

cheer, an - oth - er show please. Cle - ver A - mos,

you're so fa-mous,   Watch him swing-ing,   fin-gers cling-ing.

Cle-ver A-mos,   you're so fa-mous,   Cle-ver A - mos   Ape.

Remember a dot *under* or *above* a note makes it staccato.

A dot *at the side* of the note means the note is half as long again.

e.g. ♩. = ♩ + ♪ = 1½ beats
      1   ½

𝅗𝅥. = 𝅗𝅥 + ♩ = 3 beats
    2   1

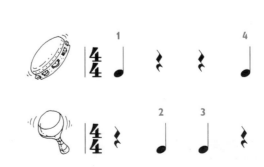

17

Geraldine's birthday gift

Count 5 before you start.

three me‑tres, four, five me‑tres, six me‑tres, seven me‑tres more,

eight me ‑ tres long with a fringe on each end, a

long, long, long gift for a long neck ‑ ed friend.

The natural sign ♮ tells
you to play C not C♯.

my   my

birth ‑ day   birth ‑ day

19

Danielle's ditty

Count 3.

Remember not to play
the second note if it is
the same as the first
note and is tied to it.

Do things for each o - ther

My name is Dan - i - elle Deer. I'm glad that you are all here. I some-tim

used to feel sad — but now I nev - er feel bad. It's great to have friends a

do things for each o - ther, when you're feel-ing low or on your own._____ It

great to have friends and do things for each o - ther, when you have good friends you're not a - lone.

Here is our new note B♭ (B flat).

It sounds a bit higher than A and a bit lower than B.

The B flat sign is put at the beginning of a tune to show that all the Bs are played as B flats.

B♭

left hand

right hand

1st finger

3rd finger

thumb underneath

1st finger

thumb underneath over hole

Ber - tram comes to have a chat. If you can play the note B flat, I'll eat my hat! B flat fin - ger - ing is 1 3 1. Re - - mem - ber this, re - mem - ber this and watch the fun!

21

Sunshine

1. Sun-shine, let's go and play out-side. Sun-shine, have fun all day play-ing
2. Sea-side, let's go a-way to-day. Sea-side, let's go on ho-li-day,

down by the pool, it's so spark-ling and ting-ling and cool, _____ now that sum-mer's
see good friends far and wide, hop-ing the sun does-n't hide, _____ now that sum-mer's

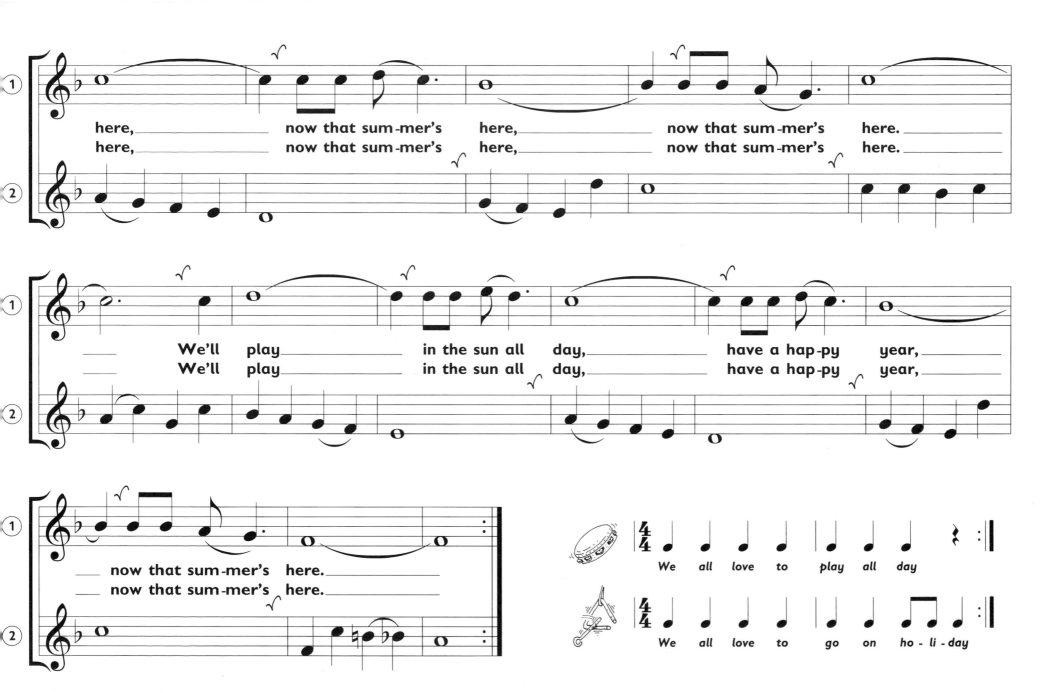

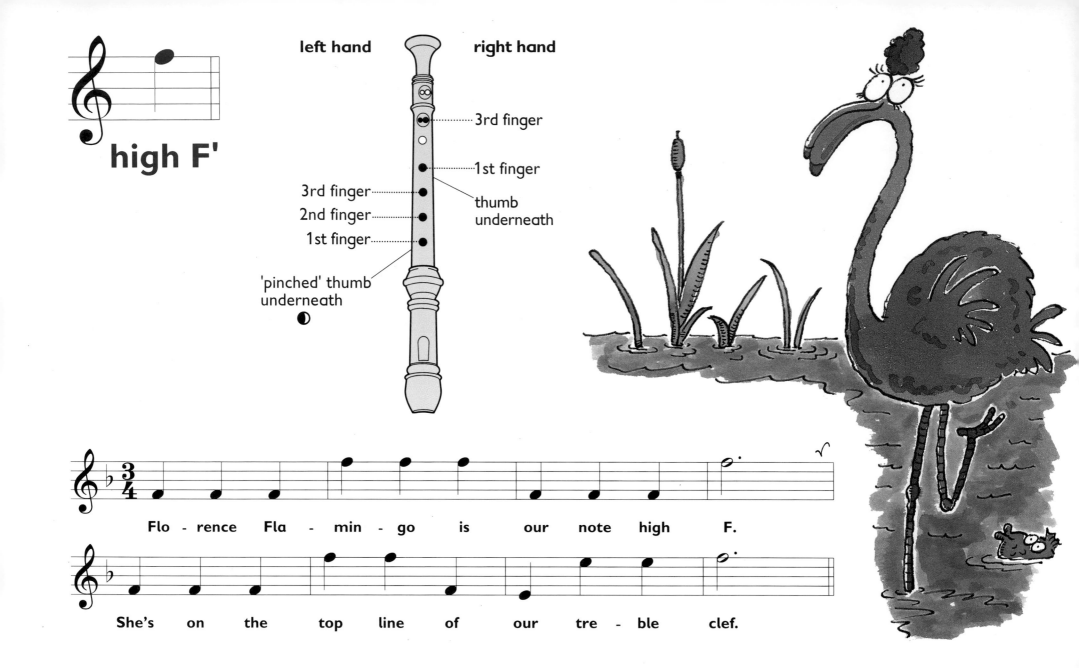

high F'

left hand

right hand

3rd finger

1st finger

3rd finger

2nd finger

1st finger

thumb underneath

'pinched' thumb underneath

Flo - rence Fla – min - go is our note high F.

She's on the top line of our tre - ble clef.

Flo's calypso

Play up to the repeat signs :‖ and then go back to the beginning. Play the tune again but miss out bar ⌐1 and play bar ⌐2 to finish the tune.

1. Flo-rence Fla-min-go, Flo-rence Fla-min-go, oh what a mouth-ful
2. My legs are long and look ve-ry thin but when we have ra-ces

just call me Flo! I have white fea-thers all tinged with pink and
I some-times win. I of-ten like to stand in a daze and

stand in the lake to have a good drink.
dream of our hap-py ho-li-days.

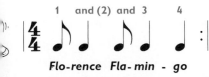

Flo-rence Fla-min-go

Off we go with Denzel

Count 1 2, 3 4 1 and 2 and 3 and (4)

1. We've been to Lon - don, Leeds and Leices - ter, Car - diff, Crewe and Che - ster, Pe - ter - bor - ough, Ports - mouth and
2. We've been to Ab - er - deen and Ash - ford, Ex - et - er and Ox - ford, Mid - dles - bor - ough, More - cambe and

Poole. Now we're off to Gill - ing - ham, Bris - tol, Bath and Bir - ming - ham, Glas - gow, Gains - bor - ough and
Mull. Now we're off to Nott - ing - ham, Cov - en - try and Chipp - en - ham, Hor - sell, Harr - o - gate and

This song can be played by 3 recorders or the 3rd part could be played by a xylophone, chime bars or even a plucked violin.
You will need the notes D, E, F#, G, A, B, C#', D'.

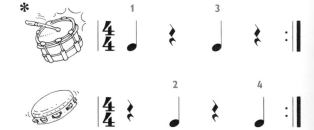

27

Fingering chart

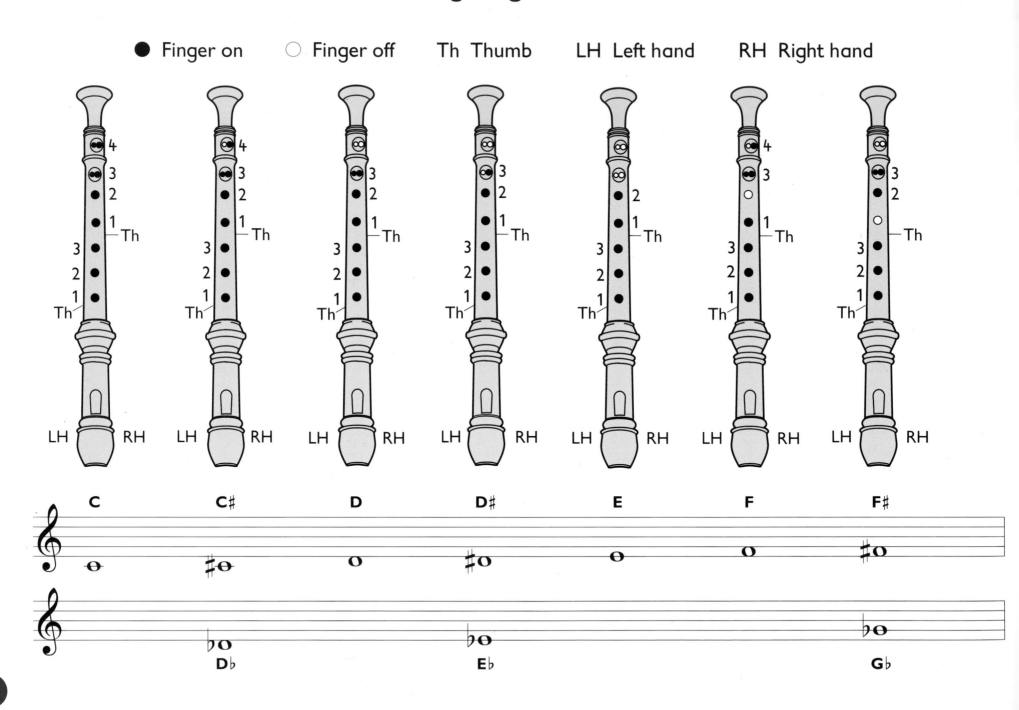

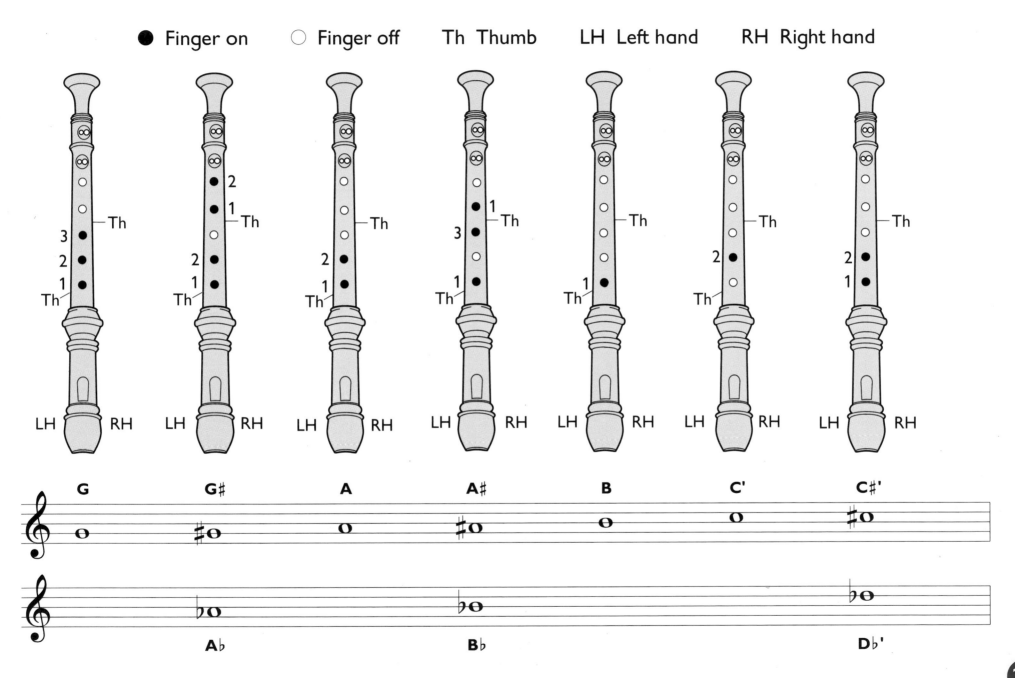

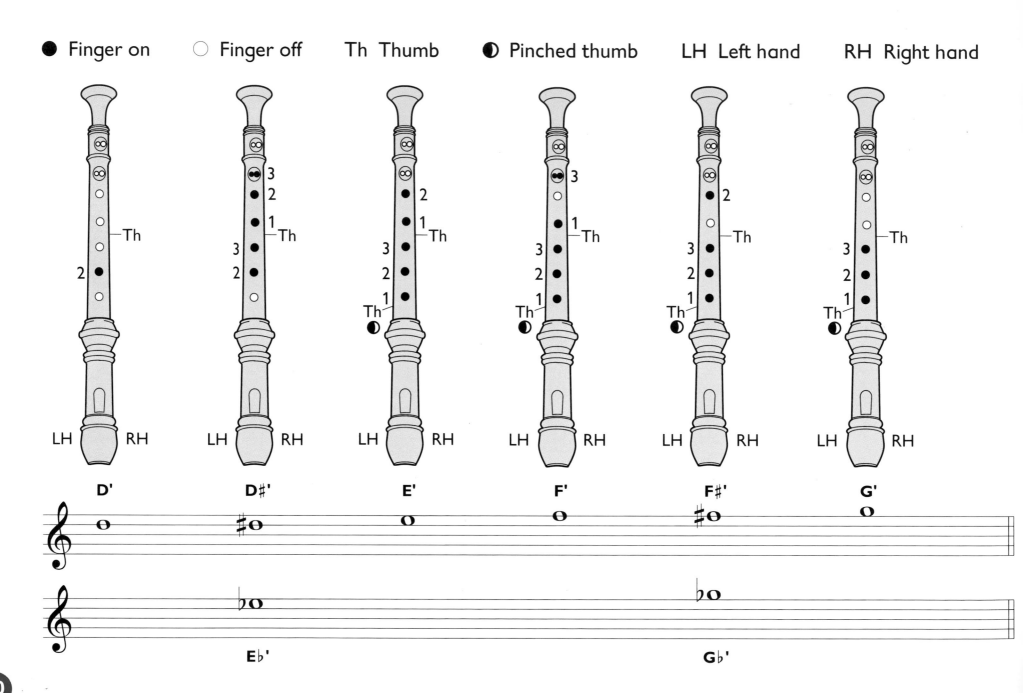

NOTES FOR TEACHERS

Music in the National Curriculum

The National Curriculum for Music refers to pupils' understanding and enjoyment of music. As with Book 1, *Franzo Frog and his Friends Book 2* continues to provide an enjoyable experience for children. It introduces more sophisticated songs and two-part pieces which give children experience of melodies weaving together, adding texture and harmony. There is further explanation of musical notation and terms as well as the dynamics and phrasing of performance. All are carefully phased and designed to fit with the children's level of playing. Again, all the tunes and words are original and especially written to appeal to both boys and girls to play and sing.

The musical activities in the books are designed to provide good musical experiences which help to fulfil the Attainment Targets of the National Curriculum for Music: Performing, Composing, Listening and Appraising.

Performing

Playing the recorder gives children the opportunity to perform on a musical instrument, either individually or in groups, and to take part in ensemble playing with other instruments. All the pieces in this book are singable songs and there are also lots of examples of ways of playing together with percussion accompaniment.

Composing

The most exciting new element in the National Curriculum is children's composition of their own music which was introduced in Book 1. When they use Book 2, they will be ready to develop composition further, making up their own rhythms, tunes and songs. The book helps children to formulate their musical ideas for the voice, then the recorder, as well as on percussion instruments. It gives a starting point and a stimulus for composition which can be developed with the teacher's help.

Listening and appraising

Performing in a group of different players and singers helps children to listen to each other and to **develop awareness of other performers**. The songs provide a good range of musical styles from calypso to blues and syncopation. They are carefully written to provide children with good examples of phrasing, rhythmical patterns, melodic lines and musical structure. Children should be encouraged to listen to and appraise their own performances and compositions.

Using Book 2

- As in Book 1, the recorder in the pictures appears upside-down to give children the correct **left-right orientation** for the hands with the recorder in the playing position. You will find that children are able to match the hand positions more easily than in traditional recorder books.

- The **pinched thumb** (see page 10) can be difficult for some children at first. It needs a firmer tonguing action than the gentle tonguing of the low notes. Encourage children to keep trying – they may mistake the high note for an unwanted squeak at first. Try blowing a few low Es, then try a high E' with the pinched thumb. Once learned, other high notes follow in the same way.

- Encourage children to blow gently and to listen to the musical quality of the sounds they make.

- The fingering chart is there to remind children of the notes learned in Books 1 and 2. It also shows additional notes which children may need for playing other music.

- 6/8 time is introduced on page 11. Strictly, this is compound time – two lots of three quavers – and there should be two beats in the bar. However, for teaching purposes, it is simplified so that six quavers in each bar are counted. When the song is known and it can be played at a moderate speed, children can be encouraged to count the two main beats, instead of six, on the first and fourth quavers.

- The natural sign ♮ shown on page 18 in part 2 is strictly not necessary as C♯ has only been used in part 1, but it is included in order to make the teaching point. Similarly, the sharp sign ♯ used before the C on page 27 is not necessary, but is included to act as a reminder.

- Breathing marks are introduced on page 6. They are only suggestions and will obviously vary according to the speed the tune is played. Where there are rests with natural breaks for breathing, for example in 'Ebenezer Elephant's aerobics', the breathing marks are omitted.

- In the last song, 'Off we go with Denzel', try to substitute your own home town to make it fun for the children.

Ensemble playing (playing together)

- In this book children are given more opportunity to play together. As in Book 1 there are suggested percussion accompaniments with words to help with the rhythms. The **percussion parts** are only suggestions and children can be encouraged to make up their own accompaniments, or to use other instruments.

- Children are now introduced to playing **two recorder parts**. Most of the songs in this book are in two parts. It is better if these are learned separately as independent tunes, then put together when the children can play each one confidently.

- In ensemble playing it can be difficult to keep all the parts together. So it is very important for the teacher, or ensemble leader, to count the **number of beats** before beginning to play and to keep the beat going all the way through.

- When performing each song, it is a good idea to bring in percussion, recorder and voices separately. Count the number of beats in the bar first, then bring in the percussion for two bars before counting in the recorder parts. At the end of the song the percussion can continue for two bars, then recorders can repeat the song with the addition of the voices.

Composition

In Book 1 there are suggestions for encouraging children's composition. This is continued in Book 2.

- Let children play around with the notes that they know and make up tunes. They can be encouraged to make up pieces at home and bring them to school to play to the group. These tunes can be memorised, recorded on tape, or written down for the group to share. The notes can be written using letter names, or the children's own notation systems. Formal staff notation is not a requirement of the National Curriculum until Key Stage 3.

- The children's own tunes can make a **bank of practice pieces** for the group to supplement the songs in the book, until the teacher feels that children are ready to progress to learning the next note.

- Children can use the words of the songs in the book to make up new tunes. Percussion can then be added. As you work through the book encourage children to make up tunes which can be played by ear, written down, or recorded. Starting with a sentence or a phrase can give a rhythmic basis for a simple composition. Use the rhythms and tunes in the book as examples for children to model their own compositions.

- **Group improvisation**, with percussion, can be encouraged, taking themes from the songs, such as Movement and flight ('Clarissa's song', page 15) or Rhythmic patterns ('Amos the acrobat', page 16).

Making and performing a musical

Book 2 is a collection of songs based on the characters from Book 1. There is no story-line. However, children can make their own story, using any of the songs, to create a little musical. Children's own compositions can also be included, either melodic ones with voice or purely rhythmic. Group improvisations using percussion can be used to accompany the story narrative.

Heinemann Educational Publis
Halley Court, Jordan Hill, Oxf
OX2 8EJ
a division of Reed Educationa
Professional Publishing Ltd

MELBOURNE AUCKLAND
FLORENCE PRAGUE MAD
ATHENS SINGAPORE TOK
CHICAGO SAO PAULO
PORTSMOUTH NH MEXIC
IBADAN GABORONE
JOHANNESBURG KAMPAL
NAIROBI

© Heather Ward, 1996

First published 1996
99 98 97 96
10 9 8 7 6 5 4 3 2 1

**British Library Catalogui
in Publication Data**
A catalogue record for this bc
is available from the British Lib

ISBN 0 435 80984 9

Illustrated by Trevor Dunton,
Jeff Edwards and Simon Smith
Designed by Susan Clarke
Music setting by Halstan & Co
Printed and bound in
Great Britain by Halstan & Co